To all my students,
past, present, and future...dream big!

**www.mascotbooks.com**

*Cooking with Mr. C.*

**For more information, please contact:**
Mascot Books
560 Herndon Parkway #120
Herndon, VA 20170
info@mascotbooks.com

Library of Congress Control Number: 2015917914

CPSIA Code: PRT1215A
ISBN: 978-1-63177-258-0

Printed in the United States

# Cooking with Mr. C.

## by John Contratti

### Illustrated by Romney Vasquez

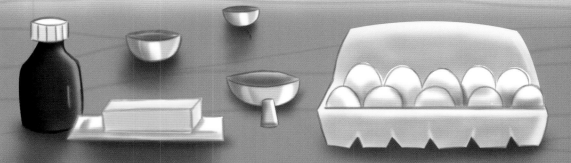

Summer flew by for Scottie Turner. It was the first day of a new school year, and Scottie was excited to meet his new fourth grade teacher. Scottie's sister was in Mr. C.'s class two years ago and she said he had a special way of teaching.

When Scottie and his classmates entered the classroom, Mr. C. was ready and waiting. "Welcome to fourth grade, boys and girls. As you can see, I have a very exciting year planned for all of us."

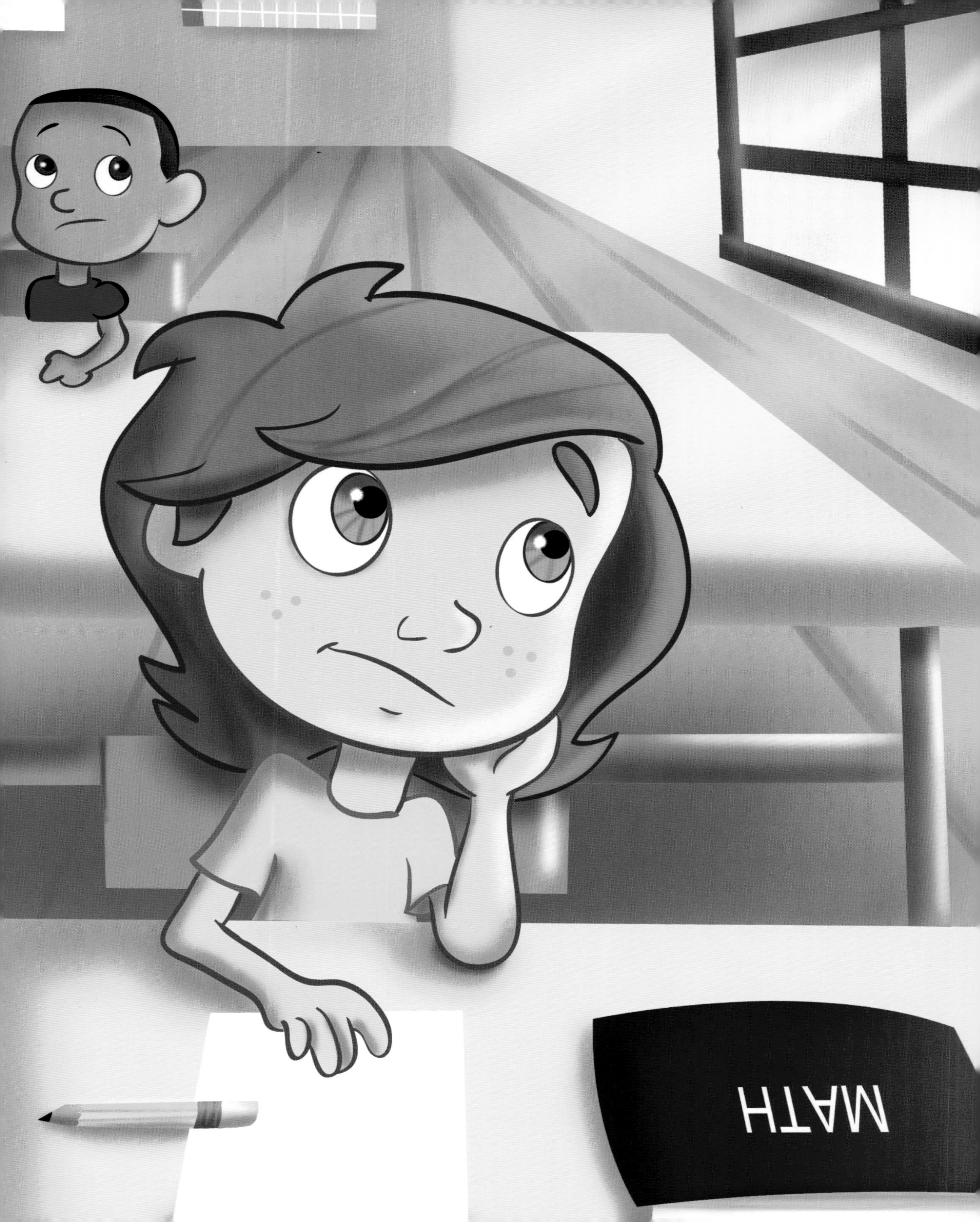
MATH

"I'd like to start today's math lesson by adding some fractions," said Mr. C. The whole class groaned. Scottie couldn't believe they were going to do math on the first day of school. *I wish it was still summer,* Scottie thought. *I'd rather be outside playing baseball.*

"We're going to make chocolate chip cookies," announced Mr. C. "Cookies and fractions?" asked Cynthia Stone.

"Cookies and fractions!" said Mr. C. "Now I just need an assistant."

Mr. C. called Scottie up to the front of the class. *Just my luck!* Scottie thought.

"Please measure out a 1/2 cup of flour and a 1/2 cup of sugar," instructed Mr. C. Scottie had never used measuring cups before. Lucky for him, all four cups were labeled. Scottie measured out the flour and sugar and put both ingredients into the bowl.

"How much flour and sugar did Scottie put in the bowl all together?" asked Mr. C.

Cynthia Stone was the first to put up her hand. "One cup!" she proudly exclaimed.

"That's correct!" replied Mr. C. "A 1/2 plus another 1/2, equals 1 whole."

1/4 cup,

1/

"This is fun!" Scottie said as he mixed all the ingredients together and finished up the recipe. "I never knew I could learn about fractions with measuring cups!"

The best part of class was when Scottie and his classmates got to eat the chocolate chip cookies.

Every day was an adventure in Mr. C.'s class. What would he teach next? How would he teach it?

As the year went on, Scottie's problem solving skills in math improved every day. Also, with all the measuring he was doing, he quickly became an expert at fractions!

Name: Scottie Turne

A+

FRACTIONS TEST

1. _____

2. _____

Scottie didn't just learn about fractions and measurements, he learned about sequencing, too. By creating something as easy as a peanut butter and jelly sandwich, Scottie learned the importance of knowing what to do first, second, third, and last in a sequence. *This is just like baseball,* Scottie thought. *You have to know where you're running next.*

 Scottie was learning how to cook and he didn't even realize it! He just loved eating his experiments.

Mr. C.'s special way of teaching caught the attention of well-known chefs. Scottie and his classmates loved when Mr. C. brought famous chefs to the classroom. The class got to interview them and best of all, cook with them. Together they mixed, measured, and created all kinds of foods from all over the world.

One day while measuring out a new recipe, Scottie got to thinking about what he wanted to be when he grew up. *I've always wanted to be a baseball player, but cooking is fun, too.*

Scottie raised his hand. "Mr. C., can you be more than one thing when you grow up?"

"Of course you can!" Mr. C. replied. "I come to school every day like you and teach my class but I'm also a cook. I'm a teacher and a cook!"

"So I could be a baseball player and a cook?" Scottie asked.

"Yes!" said Mr. C. "That's a great recipe for your future! Always remember, every recipe has more than one ingredient, so you can have lots of ingredients in your recipe for life."

On the last day of school, everyone wished each other a great summer.

# ABOUT THE AUTHOR

John Contratti has been an elementary school teacher for twenty-five years and is also a professional cook. He has cooked on the Hallmark cooking show *Mad Hungry With Lucinda Scala Quinn* which was produced by Martha Stewart. He has also appeared on the television dramas *Royal Pains* and *The Americans*. He has a hugely successful cooking blog called *Cooking With Mr. C.* He is a big supporter of the organizations Children's Health Fund, Broadway Cares, and Keen Company. Mr. Contratti resides in New York.